The Torch Runner

Dina Anastasio

SCHOLASTIC INC.
New York Toronto London Auckland Sydney
Mexico City New Delhi Hong Kong Buenos Aires

For Liam Rowe

**Illustrations by
Philippe Lechien**

The text in this edition has been revised from the original edition.

Copyright © 2005, 1999 by Scholastic Inc.
Illustrations copyright © 2005 by Philippe Lechien.
All rights reserved. Published by Scholastic Inc.
Printed in the U.S.A.

ISBN 0-439-66702-X

4 5 6 7 8 9 10   23   12 11 10 09 08

Contents

Danny's father wants him to train for the Olympics. But Danny doesn't want to.

1 The Runner

Danny Paz looked at the clock. It was seven A.M. The sun was shining through the window by his bed. What a great morning for a run!

Danny put on his shorts and went outside. He stretched a few times and took off. He loved to run in the morning. The sun was bright, but it wasn't too hot yet.

He loved watching the world wake up. He loved the quiet. He loved seeing the first shop open its doors. He loved watching the driver unload the bread truck. It was so peaceful.

He ran for an hour before he got tired. Then he walked home slowly. His father was waiting for him in the kitchen.

"Did you have a nice run?" Mr. Paz asked.

Danny nodded.

"You're a good runner," his father said, bringing Danny his breakfast.

Danny **shrugged** and bit into his eggs. He was starving. When he was done, he went into the living room and turned on the TV. He wanted to watch the sports news before he went to school.

The woman on TV was talking about the **Olympics**. The Summer Olympics were going to be in Los Angeles. That's where Danny lived.

"I wonder who will carry the **torch** this year," his father yelled from the kitchen.

"Lots of people," Danny yelled back.

Danny didn't care about the Olympic

torch. But his father cared more about the torch than any of the sports **events**.

Danny had heard about the torch all his life. He knew everything about it.

He knew that the torch was always lit in Olympia, Greece. He knew that it was carried by runners from Greece to the city where the Olympics were taking place.

His father had told him about the 1968 Olympics in Mexico City. The torch had been carried from Greece to Spain. In Spain, a runner had carried it onto a ship. The ship then brought it to Mexico. Then other runners carried the torch into Mexico City.

"That torch went the same way that Christopher Columbus went," his father had told him, again and again. "Those runners carried it all the way to North America!"

"You could really be a great runner, Danny," his father said now. "If you worked hard enough, maybe you could be in the Olympics in a few years."

Mr. Paz had said this before. He had said it too many times. And every time Danny said the same thing back.

"No thanks, Dad," he said. "I run for the fun of it. I don't care about being in the Olympics."

His father usually stopped asking him then. But only for a while. He always tried again later.

This time it was different. This time his father wouldn't stop. He came into the living room and sat down next to Danny.

"Couldn't you just try?" he asked.

Danny turned away. Why couldn't his father just leave him alone? Why couldn't his father understand that Danny liked running at his own speed?

"I saw a coach I used to know," his father went on. "He says he'd like to meet you. He used to train Olympic runners."

"No, Dad," Danny said.

"Couldn't you just see him?"

"No, Dad. I said I don't want to."

"Could you just talk to him one time?"

"Oh, okay," Danny gave in. He'd see the coach. But that would be it. He wasn't going to work with the guy.

How do you think Danny should handle this problem with his father?

Danny's father keeps pushing him. Is the coach going to start pushing him, too?

2 The Coach

The coach was sitting on a bench when Danny and his father got to the track. He stood up and shook their hands.

"I'm Joe Brown," he said. "Your dad says you want to run at the Olympics."

Danny ran the toe of his shoe through the dirt. He shrugged. He really wanted to say, "No way!" But he didn't want to make his father mad.

"He'd like to try," his father said.

The coach didn't answer Danny's father. He looked at Danny carefully.

"Your father told me that you're a really great runner," Mr. Brown said.

"I like to run," Danny said. "I don't know if I'm 'great.'"

"He's a great runner," his father said.

Danny shrugged again. What could he say? He wanted to say, "I can't be a great runner because I don't want to be." But his father and the coach wouldn't like that.

The coach looked at him. He didn't say anything for a long time. After a while, he turned to Mr. Paz. "I'd like to talk to your son alone," he said.

Mr. Paz frowned. Then he walked over to a bench and sat down.

"You don't want to train for the Olympics, do you?" Mr. Brown said.

"Not really," Danny said. "I just like to run."

"Then what are you doing here?"

"My dad talked me into it."

Danny felt mad at his father again.

"There's no need to get mad about it," Mr. Brown said. "You can relax now."

Danny relaxed and smiled.

"Sorry," he said. "It's just that Dad has this thing about the Olympics. He's really into the torch. I guess he wants me to be an Olympic runner some day. I'm not sure why."

The coach thought for a minute. Then he stood up and looked down at Danny.

"And what do you want?" he asked.

Danny began to feel mad again. Hadn't he just told the coach?

"I want to run for the fun of it," he said.

"That makes sense," Mr. Brown said. "But I like your father. And he wants me to talk you into working with me."

Danny **clenched** his fists.

Mr. Brown kept talking. "But I understand that you don't want to race. Could you help me out here?"

Danny shrugged.

"Could you spend one more hour of your time with me?" Mr. Brown asked. "Could you come back tomorrow morning at seven? I'd like to see you run."

"I run near my house at seven," Danny said.

"Then come after school. Just let me see how fast you are."

"I guess I can do that," Danny sighed. He stood up and started to walk away.

"Hey, Danny," the coach called.

Danny looked back.

"Thanks," the coach said.

Why do you think Danny's father wants him to run in the Olympics?

There's a lot Danny doesn't know about his father.

3 The Secret

Danny went back to the track the next day. He didn't want to, but he went anyway. He felt like he had to. The coach was waiting for him.

"I've been thinking about you and your dad," the coach said. "I want to talk with you. But first, let me see you run."

It was hot. Danny hated running when it was hot. And he hated running on a track.

He liked running because of all the things he got to see. He liked seeing people. He liked seeing store windows. He liked crossing the street before the light

turned red. He liked running fast around corners and stepping over the same cracks every day.

He started to run. At first, he ran fast. He knew that was what the coach wanted to see. But then he slowed down. He didn't care about the coach. He didn't care about being fast.

"You can stop now," Mr. Brown said as Danny ran past him.

Danny walked back to the bench.

"Your father's right," Mr. Brown said. "You could be good. But no one can be a great runner if they don't want to be."

"I don't want to be," Danny said.

"That's up to you," the coach agreed. "I can try to help your dad understand."

"Thanks, Coach," Danny said. "That would be great." He turned to go home.

"I'd also like to help you understand

your father," Mr. Brown added.

Danny stopped walking. "What do you mean?" he asked.

"You know that your dad is very **private**. He doesn't talk to people about his own life," Mr. Brown said.

Danny frowned. "Yeah. I know. But what does that have to do with anything?" he asked.

"I know why your dad wants you to be in the Olympics," Mr. Brown went on. "You said he loves the torch. Do you know why?"

"No," Danny said.

"You know he's from Mexico City."

Danny nodded. Sure. He knew that.

"Well, your dad carried the Olympic torch in the Mexico City Olympics."

Danny couldn't believe it. His father had been a torch runner! Why hadn't he ever told Danny that?

Mr. Brown seemed to know what

Danny was thinking.

"Maybe he doesn't like to talk about it, Danny. Maybe he's still sad that he stopped running.

"He was a teenager when he carried the torch. After that, he moved to Los Angeles to train with me.

"He loved carrying that torch. He loved it so much that he wanted to be an Olympic runner.

"But then all kinds of things happened in his life. He got married. Then you were born. He was so busy that he stopped running. I guess he wants to pass his dream on to you."

Danny didn't speak for a while. Then he said, "I wish he had told me."

Mr. Paz tells Danny about the 1968 Olympics in Mexico City.

4 The Torch

Danny talked to his father at dinner that night. He asked him about the torch.

"Why didn't you tell me you carried the Olympic torch?" he said.

"It was a long time ago," his father said. "I guess I forgot."

"You didn't forget, Dad," he said. "You talk about that torch all the time. But you never said you carried it. Why?"

His father thought for a few minutes. He played with his food for a while. Then he poured a glass of water. He drank it and then turned to Danny.

"I can't really answer that. I guess I'm

just not very good at talking about myself," he said.

"Well, what was it like? How did it feel to run with the torch?" Danny asked.

Mr. Paz stared out the window. He had a funny look in his eyes. Danny could tell that he was back there on that street in Mexico City. He was holding the torch high above his head.

"It was just about the greatest thing that ever happened to me," Mr. Paz said.

"How did they choose you? I mean, did you have to try out or something?"

"No," his father said. "I just wrote a letter and asked if I could be one of the runners. I told them I wanted to be part of Columbus's trip. I got picked. Who knows why?"

"How far did you run?" Danny asked.

"Only a mile. Not far. The runner before me passed me the torch, and I took

off. The crowds next to the roads kept screaming and cheering. They were everywhere. It was like running inside a tunnel of happy people. I'd never felt like that before. It was amazing."

"I guess that made you want to be in the Olympics," Danny said.

His father looked at him and grinned. "Mr. Brown's been telling my secrets," he laughed. "Yes, I did."

"Maybe that's why you want me to be in the Olympics now," Danny said.

Mr. Paz thought about it for a minute. "Maybe so," he said. "I never really thought about that."

Why was being a torch runner so important to Mr. Paz?

Danny finds a way to make his father happy.

5 Side by Side

Mr. Paz stopped talking about the torch after that. But Danny couldn't stop thinking about it.

He wished that he could run in the Olympics for his father.

Danny loved his father. He wanted to do something nice for him. But he just couldn't do it.

One day, Danny went to see Mr. Brown at his home. Mr. Brown invited him in and gave him a glass of soda. "What's up?" he asked.

"My father told me about carrying the

torch," Danny said. "I think it was hard for him to talk about it, but he did. His story gave me an idea. I think being a torch runner would be really cool."

"You don't have to change your mind to make your father happy," the coach said.

"I'm not," Danny said. "I still don't want to train for the Olympics. But running through the streets with the torch would be great. Do you think that I could try out?"

"I'm not sure," Mr. Brown said. "It's late. But you could ask. And I could help. I know people who work for the Olympics. It always helps to know people."

But Danny wasn't listening. He was thinking about something. He had a great idea.

"Look," he said. "What if my dad and I both carried the torch? We could carry it together, side by side.

"They might choose us if they knew about my dad. We could tell them how he carried the torch in the Mexico City Olympics. What do you think? Do you think that might work?"

"I think it's a very good idea," Mr. Brown said. "In fact, it's a great idea."

And so, one day that summer, Danny and his father carried the Olympic torch. Side by side, they ran through the streets of Los Angeles as crowds of people cheered.

Do you think Danny did the right thing? How do you think his father felt? How did Danny feel?

Glossary

clenched *(verb)* closed tightly

events *(noun)* things that happen. In this story, *events* are games or sports contests.

Olympics *(noun)* sports contests held every four years, each time in a different city

private *(adjective)* keeping to yourself

shrugged *(verb)* raised your shoulders to show doubt

torch *(noun)* a light or flame carried in the hand